Time-Life Books